D0943995

Christmas Stories That Never Grow Old

editor
van b. hooper

Contents

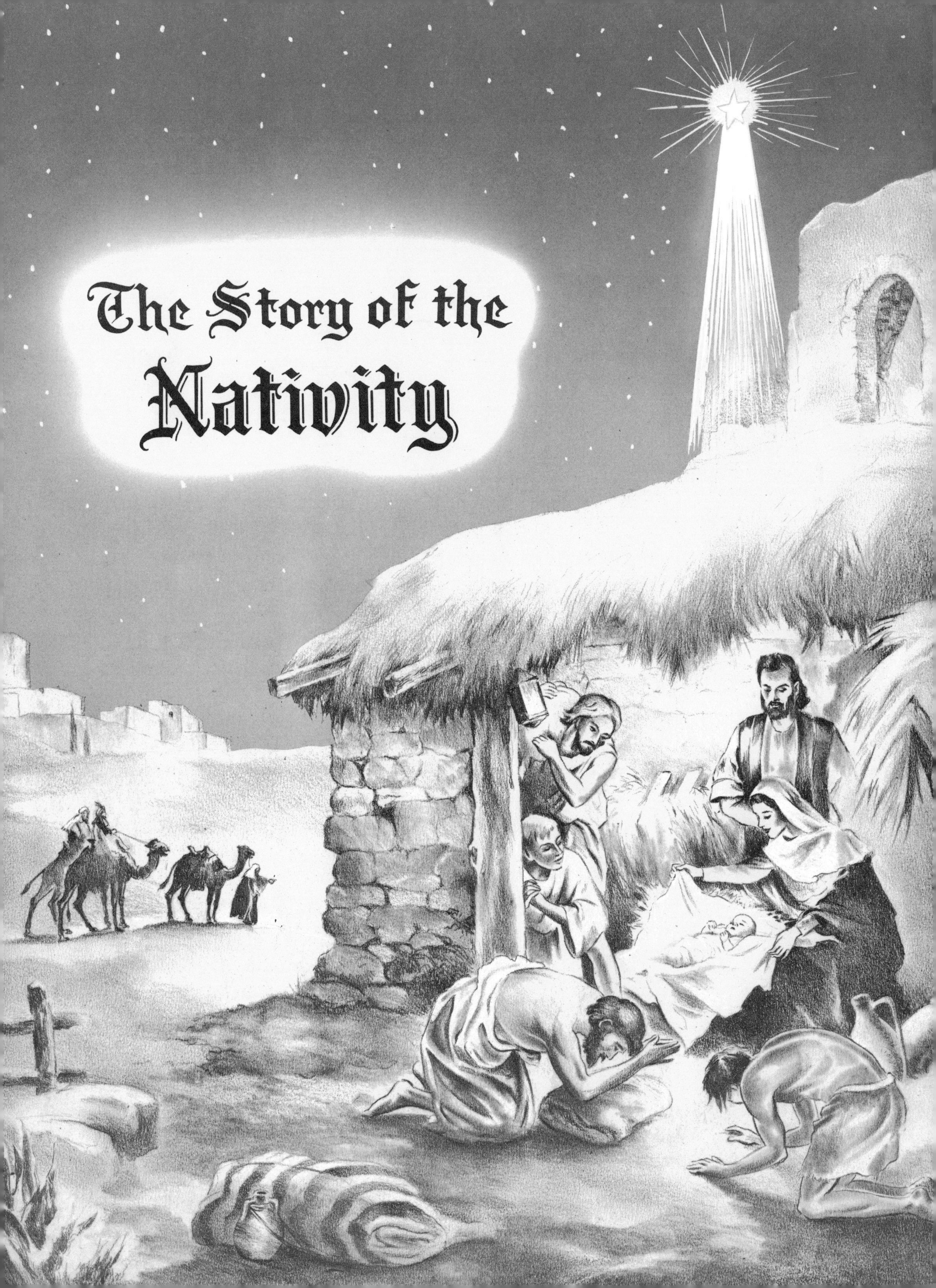
The Story of the
Nativity

The oldest and most beautiful of all stories is the life of Mary, Joseph, and their son — Jesus.

For centuries and centuries, the Jews had waited for the Messiah promised to them by Jehovah. Patiently had they waited – and the promise and dream was fulfilled. Faith, which had grown dim during the years, was revived under the words of John, the forerunner.

As it is written in the prophets, Behold, I send my messenger before thy face, which shall prepare thy way before thee. The voice of one crying in the wilderness, Prepare ye the way of the Lord, make his paths straight.

Men and women bowed down in worship, repenting their sins while they awaited the Anointed One.

An angel of the Lord came to Mary, saying: *Hail, thou, that art highly favoured, the Lord is with thee: blessed art thou among women. Fear not, Mary: for thou hast found favour with God. And behold, thou shall conceive in thy womb, and bring forth a son, and shalt call his name Jesus.*

And while Joseph was alone in thought, an angel of heaven appeared to him in a dream, saying: *Joseph, thou son of David, fear not to take unto thee Mary thy wife: for that which is conceived in her is of the Holy Ghost. And she shall bring forth a son, and thou shall call his name Jesus: for he shall save his people from their sins.*

Then Joseph, awakened from sleep, did as the angel bid, and went unto his wife.

At this time, Caesar Augustus, ruler of the land, sent out a decree that all who lived there were to be taxed. Joseph and Mary were living in Nazareth, and the journey to Bethlehem was long and hard. Mary rode on a donkey while Joseph walked ahead, leading the donkey.

They were tired and weary when they reached Bethlehem, and the city was crowded. There was no room for them in the inns. The innkeepers saw that they were very poor, and did not want to bother with them. Finally, they knocked at the door of an inn at the edge of town. This innkeeper was a very kind man, and although he had no room in the inn, he said that they might sleep in the stable with the animals. Very thankful were Joseph and Mary for this shelter.

Inside the humble stable, Joseph gathered some of the fragrant hay and made a soft bed in one corner for Mary. She lay down and soon fell asleep in this strange place. The animals were curious to see who was sharing their home, and gathered about Mary and Joseph.

And she brought forth her first-born son, and wrapped him in swaddling clothes, and laid him in a manger; because there was no room for them in the inn.

A great light shone in the sky -- and the shepherds in the field were afraid, for never before had they seen such a sight. An angel from the heavens above came to comfort them, saying:

Behold, I bring you good tidings of great joy, which shall be to all people. For unto you is born this day in the city of David a saviour, which is Christ the Lord. And this shall be a sign unto you; Ye shall find the babe wrapped in swaddling clothes, lying in a manger.

And suddenly there was with the angel a multitude of the heavenly host praising God and saying, Glory to God in the highest, and on earth peace, good will toward men.

As the shepherds came to the stable and found Mary and Joseph, and the baby lying in the manger, they fell on their knees and prayed to the child who was their King. In great exultation they returned to their flock, telling other shepherds they met about the child, Jesus, their King, who was born in a manger.

In far off Persia, Three Wise Men were looking in the sky and saw a strange star. As they watched, the star told them of the baby, Jesus, who was King of the world. The wise men hurriedly packed their finest gifts on their camels and embarked upon their journey to Bethlehem to see the Christ Child.

It took many days before they arrived in Bethlehem. They came, saying: *Where is he that is born King of the Jews? for we have seen his star in the east, and are come to worship him.*

And when they were come into the house, they saw the young child with Mary, his mother. They, too, fell on their knees and prayed, presenting gifts of gold, frankincense, and myrrh to the child of Love.

Now, after the Wise Men left, an angel of the Lord appeared to Joseph in a dream, saying: *Arise, and take the young child and his mother, and flee into Egypt, and be thou there until I bring thee word: for Herod will seek the young child to destroy him. When he arose, he took the young child and his mother, by night, and departed into Egypt.*

There they lived until word came that Herod was dead. *And he came and dwelt in a city called Nazareth: that it might be fulfilled which was spoken by the prophets, he shall be called a Nazarene.*

The Little
Match Girl

A long, long time ago—on a bitter cold New Year's eve—a poor little girl with bare feet was trudging along through the cold deep snow.

Yes, her feet were bare—because she had no real shoes—and the large slippers some one had given her had been lost when she ran to get out of the way of a cart—and a naughty boy ran away with one of them.

So she was walking in the bitter, bitter cold snow and her poor little bare feet were red and blue with cold.

In her apron she was carrying a lot of matches that she was trying to sell for a penny a box.

No one had bought any from her all day long—and the poor little thing was shivering and hungry—but she was afraid to go home—because her cruel foster father would beat her—for she had not sold even a half-penny of matches all day long.

She looked into the bright cheerful windows of homes as she walked by—everyone seemed so warm and comfortable and happy—everyone except the poor little match girl.

She saw a beautiful trimmed Christmas tree in one—from another came the tempting aroma of roast goose—and she was so very hungry.

It was getting colder—and snowing harder—and it was now real dark—when she huddled in a corner between two buildings to try to keep warm.

She took one little match from a box and lit it to warm her frozen fingers. How brightly it sputtered—in its light she seemed to see a big warm stove—how warm and cozy it was—but when the match burned out—the stove disappeared—and she was colder than ever.

She struck a second match—and before her was a big table—with glistening white table

cloth—there was a huge roast duck—and apples—and cake and warm milk—and she was so happy because she was so terribly hungry. Then just when she was reaching for the roast duck—the match burned out—and, then she was colder and more hungry than ever.

She lighted another match—and lo!—there was the most beautiful Christmas tree she had ever seen—full of shiny toys and sparkling candles, candies and everything nice.

The beautiful candles rose higher and higher —until they were only stars in the sky—then one of them fell.

"That falling star means some one is dying" she said to herself—"my dear grandmother used to tell me that."

She quickly lit another match—and another —then a whole hand full—and right in the bright glow—so dazzling and bright, and so kind and loving stood her dear old grandmother with outstretched arms.

"Grandmother!" she cried—"please take me with you! I know you will go away when the match burns out—just like the roast goose and the warm stove and the Christmas tree did."

She quickly lighted the whole box of matches —because she did not want her grandmother to go. The matches burned with a blaze that was as light as day—her grandmother had never seemed so beautiful—and as she took the poor little match girl in her arms she flew up with her in brightness and joy, high, so very high—and there was no cold and no hunger—and no sorrow—and—no matches to sell—for they were in heaven.

In the morning, people passed by and saw the poor little girl still huddled between the buildings, with burned matches about her.

Adapted from
HANS CHRISTIAN ANDERSEN

Many years ago a little girl, who was wondering about the existence of Santa Claus, wrote this letter to the New York Sun.

Dear Editor,
I am 8 years old. Some of my friends say there is no Santa Claus. Papa says if you see it in the Sun, it is so. Please tell me the truth, is there a Santa Claus? Virginia O'Hanlon

Dear Virginia,

Your little friends are wrong.

They have been affected by the skepticism of a skeptical age. They do not believe except what they see. They think that nothing can be which is not comprehensible by their minds. All minds, Virginia, whether they be men's or children's are little.

In this great universe of ours, man is a mere insect, an ant, in his intellect, as compared with the boundless world about him, as measured by the intelligence capable of grasping the whole of truth and knowledge.

Yes, Virginia, there is a Santa Claus. He exists as certainly as love and generosity and devotion exist, and you know that they abound and give to your life its highest beauty and joy. Alas! how dreary would be the world if there were no Santa Claus! It would be as dreary as if there were no Virginias. There would be no childlike faith then, no poetry, no romance, to make tolerable this existence. We should have no enjoyment, except in sense and sight. The eternal light with which childhood fills the world would be extinguished.

Not believe in Santa Claus! You might as well not believe in Fairies! You might get your papa to hire men to watch in chimneys on Christmas evening to catch Santa Claus, but even if they did not see Santa Claus coming down, what would that prove? Nobody sees Santa Claus, but that is no sign that there is no Santa Claus. The most real things in the world are those that neither children nor men can see.

Did you ever see Fairies dancing on the lawn? Of course not, but that's no proof that they are not there. Nobody can conceive or imagine all the wonders there are unseen and unseeable in the world.

You may tear apart the baby's rattle and see what makes the noise inside, but there is a veil covering the unseen world which not the strongest man, nor even the united strength of all the strongest men that ever lived, could tear apart. Only faith, fancy, poetry, love, romance, can push aside that curtain and view and picture the supernal beauty and glory beyond.

Is it real? Ah, Virginia, in all this world there is nothing else real and abiding.

No Santa Claus?
Thank God, he lives and he lives forever. A thousand years from now, Virginia, nay, ten times ten thousand years from now, he will continue to make glad the heart of childhood.

Francis P. Church
Editor

The original Virginia who wrote the above letter to the editor of the New York Sun in 1897, is now Mrs. Edward Douglas, assistant principal of Public School 31 in New York City.

The Gift of the Magi

O. Henry

One dollar and eighty-seven cents. That was all. And sixty cents of it was in pennies. Three times Della counted it. One dollar and eighty-seven cents. And the next day would be Christmas.

There was clearly nothing to do but flop down on the shabby little couch and howl. So Della did it.

In the vestibule below was a letter-box. Appertaining thereunto was a card bearing the name "Mr. James Dillingham Young".

The "Dillingham" had been flung to the breeze during a former period of prosperity when its possessor was being paid $30 per week. Now, when the income was shrunk to $20, the letters of "Dillingham" looked blurred. But whenever Mr. James Dillingham Young came home and reached his flat above, he was called "Jim" and greatly hugged by Mrs. James Dillingham Young, already introduced to you as Della.

Della finished her cry and attended to her cheeks with the powder rag. She stood by the window and looked out dully at a gray cat walking a gray fence in a gray backyard. Tomorrow would be Christmas Day, and she had only $1.87 with which to buy Jim a present. She had been saving every penny she could for months, with this result. Twenty dollars a week doesn't go far. Only $1.87 to buy a present for Jim.

There was a pier-glass between the windows of the room.

Suddenly Della whirled from the window and stood before the glass. Her eyes were shining brilliantly. Rapidly she pulled down her hair and let it fall to its full length.

Now, there were two possessions of the James Dillingham Youngs in which they both took a mighty pride. One was Jim's gold watch that had been his father's and his grandfather's. The other was Della's hair.

So now Della's beautiful hair fell about her, rippling and shining like a cascade of brown waters. It reached below her knee and made itself almost a garment for her. And then she did it up again nervously and quickly.

On went her old brown jacket; on went her old brown hat. With a whirl of skirts and with the brilliant sparkle still in her eyes, she fluttered out the door and down the stairs to the street.

Where she stopped the sign read: "Mme. Sofronie. Hair Goods of All Kinds." One flight up Della ran, and collected herself, panting. Madame, large, too white, chilly, hardly looked the "Sofronie"

"Will you buy my hair?" asked Della.

"I buy hair," said Madame. "Take yer hat off and let's have a sight at the looks of it."

Down rippled the brown cascade.

"Twenty dollars," said Madame, lifting the mass with a practised hand.

"Give it to me quick," said Della.

Oh, and the next two hours tripped by on rosy wings. She was ransacking the stores for Jim's present.

She found it at last. It was a platinum fob chain, simple and chaste in design. As soon as she saw it she knew that it must be Jim's. It was like him. Quietness and value — the description applied to both. Twenty-one dollars they took from her for it, and she hurried home with the 87 cents.

When Della reached home her intoxication gave way a little to prudence and reason. She got out her curling irons and lighted the gas and went to work repairing the ravages made by generosity added to love.

Within forty minutes her head was covered with tiny, close-lying curls that made her look wonderfully like a truant schoolboy.

"If Jim doesn't kill me, before he takes a second look at me, he'll say I look like a Coney Island chorus girl. But what could I do — oh! what could I do with a dollar and eighty-seven cents?"

At 7 o'clock the coffee was made and the frying pan was on the back of the stove, hot and ready to cook the chops.

Jim was never late. Then she heard his step on the stair away down on the first flight, and she turned white for just a moment. She had a habit of saying little silent prayers about the simplest everyday things, and now she whispered: "Please, God, make him think I am still pretty."

The door opened and Jim stepped in and closed it. He looked thin and very serious.

Jim stopped inside the door. His eyes were fixed upon Della and there was an expression in them that she could not read, and it terrified her. It was not anger, nor surprise, nor disapproval, nor horror, nor any of the sentiments that she had been prepared for. He simply stared at her fixedly with that peculiar expression on his face.

Della wriggled off the table and went for him.

"Jim darling, don't look at me that way. I had my hair cut off and sold it because I couldn't have lived through Christmas without giving you a present. It'll grow out again — you won't mind, will you? I just had to do it. My hair grows awfully fast. Say 'Merry Christmas!' Jim, and let's be happy. You don't know what a nice — what a beautiful, nice gift I've got for you."

"You've cut off your hair?" asked Jim, laboriously, as if he had not arrived at that patent fact yet, even after the hardest mental labor.

"Cut it off and sold it. Don't you like me just as well, anyhow? I'm me without my hair, ain't I?"

Jim looked about the room curiously.

"You say your hair is gone?"

"You needn't look for it. It's sold, I tell you — sold and gone, too. It's Christmas Eve, boy. Be good to me, for it went for you. Maybe the hairs of my head were numbered, but nobody could ever count my love for you. Shall I put the chops on, Jim?"

Jim drew a package from his overcoat pocket and threw it upon the table.

"Don't make any mistake, Dell, about me. I don't think there's anything in the way of a haircut or a shave or a shampoo that could make me like my girl any less. But if you'll unwrap that package, you may see why you had me going a while at first."

White fingers and nimble tore at the string and paper. And then an ecstatic scream of joy; and then, alas! a quick feminine change to hysterical tears and wails, necessitating the immediate employment of all the comforting powers of the lord of the flat.

For there lay *the combs* — the set of combs, side and back —

that Della had worshipped for long in a Broadway window. Beautiful combs, pure tortoise shell, with jewelled rims — just the shade to wear in the beautiful vanished hair. They were expensive combs, she knew, and her heart had simply craved and yearned over them without the least hope of possession. And now they were hers, but the tresses that should have adorned the coveted adornments were gone.

But she hugged them to her bosom, and at length she was able to look up with dim eyes and a smile and say: "My hair grows so fast, Jim!"

And then Della leaped up like a little singed cat and cried, "Oh, oh!"

Jim had not yet seen his beautiful present. She held it out to him eagerly upon her open palm. The dull precious metal seemed to flash with a reflection of her bright and ardent spirit.

"Isn't it a dandy, Jim? I hunted all over town to find it. You'll have to look at the time a hundred times a day now. Give me your watch. I want to see how it looks on it."

Instead of obeying, Jim tumbled down on the couch and put his hands under the back of his head and smiled.

"Dell, let's put our Christmas presents away and keep 'em awhile. They're too nice to use just at present. I sold the watch to get the money to buy your combs. And now suppose you put the chops on."

The magi, as you know, were wise men — wonderfully wise men — who brought gifts to the Babe in the manger. Being wise, their gifts were no doubt wise ones, possibly bearing the privilege of exchange in case of duplication. And here I have lamely related to you the uneventful chronicle of two foolish children in a flat who most unwisely sacrificed for each other the greatest treasures of their house. But in a last word to the wise of these days, let it be said that of all who give gifts, such as they are wisest. Everywhere they are wisest. They are the magi.

The Man Who Brought The Myrrh

Shirley G. Robinson

The listening silence held its cold, sparkling arms about them, bringing Heaven close to the three tired travelers who, in spite of the excitement and wonder of the last few hours, had fallen asleep on the ground before the ebbing campfire.

Upon each countenance sleep carved a deep calmness, a serenity, a radiance which might be explained only by one who recognized the three as sages from the East who had just come from worship of the newly born King of the Jews.

Now they were on their way back to the king's palace to bring Herod news of the Child and of the place of his birth.

Beyond the hill a shimmering white light began to appear slowly, steadily. As it became brighter its radiance seemed to spread, illuminating the surrounding countryside. With a start, the travelers awakened and sat up as they heard a voice saying, "Behold."

Blinded by the brilliance and gasping with the glory of the man in the lustrous white robes, seemingly suspended on the path of light extending from the heavens, they uttered a cry of fear as of one man, and fell upon their faces.

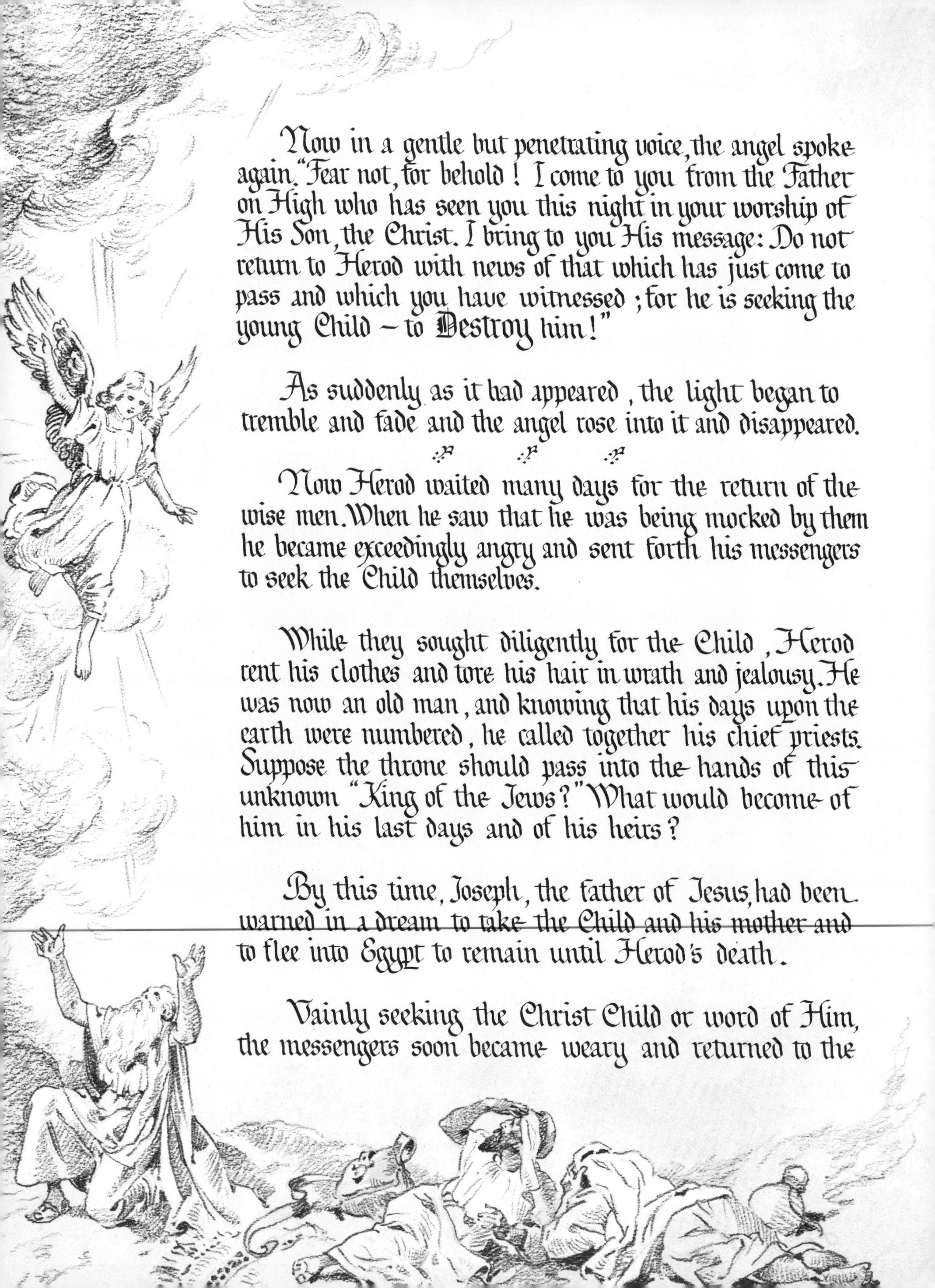

Now in a gentle but penetrating voice, the angel spoke again. "Fear not, for behold! I come to you from the Father on High who has seen you this night in your worship of His Son, the Christ. I bring to you His message: Do not return to Herod with news of that which has just come to pass and which you have witnessed; for he is seeking the young Child — to Destroy him!"

As suddenly as it had appeared, the light began to tremble and fade and the angel rose into it and disappeared.

Now Herod waited many days for the return of the wise men. When he saw that he was being mocked by them he became exceedingly angry and sent forth his messengers to seek the Child themselves.

While they sought diligently for the Child, Herod rent his clothes and tore his hair in wrath and jealousy. He was now an old man, and knowing that his days upon the earth were numbered, he called together his chief priests. Suppose the throne should pass into the hands of this unknown "King of the Jews?" What would become of him in his last days and of his heirs?

By this time, Joseph, the father of Jesus, had been warned in a dream to take the Child and his mother and to flee into Egypt to remain until Herod's death.

Vainly seeking the Christ Child or word of Him, the messengers soon became weary and returned to the king only to be sent forth again into all parts of Bethlehem and the coasts thereof with the command to slay every child of two years and under, according to the time at which Herod had first inquired of the wise men were the King was to be born.

In this manner, surely the Child's destruction would be assured!

Before the return of the commissioners, however, Herod in his great wrath fell violently ill upon his bed and died, leaving the throne to his son.

And when Joseph had received this word from God, he took the Child Jesus and his mother into Galilee, making their dwelling in a place called Nazareth that it might be fulfilled which was spoken by the prophets, "He shall be called a Nazarene."

⁂ ⁂ ⁂

The threatening silence closed in about them, bringing Heaven close to the crowd thronging about the hillside. Out of the silence a sudden cry of unimaginable anguish escaped the lips of One hanging from a rough-hewn cross at the crest of a hill.

Upon his countenance even pain carved a deep calmness, a serenity, a radiance which could be explained most fully, perhaps, by an old man who slowly, haltingly, made his way through the mocking crowd to the foot of the hill where he laid his gift of

myrrh. Then he fell down, trembling, in worship of "his King."

The crowd moved back in silence as the heavens grew darker and darker, and a deeper peace settled over the face of the One hanging from the cross as he parted his lips for the final time.... "Father, unto Thy hands, I commend my spirit."

The old man, tearfully, quietly, made his way back to the place where his camel waited.

Remembering that night years before, he thought of his two companions who had come with him to worship the Babe in the manger. What would they have thought—if they could have witnessed the scene which he had just witnessed?

Perhaps they had..... and were even now preparing their gifts of heavenly gold and frankincense for the day when they would soon worship him again.

The Juggler of Notre Dame

Anatole France

In the days when the world was young, there lived in France a man of no importance. Everyone said he was a man of no importance, and he firmly believed this himself. For he was just a poor traveling juggler, who could not read or write, who went about from town to town following the little country fairs, and performing his tricks for a few pennies a day. His name was Barnaby.

When the weather was beautiful, and people were strolling about the streets, this juggler would find a clear space in the Village Square, spread a strip of old carpet out on the cobblestones, and on it he would perform his tricks for children and grown-ups alike. Now Barnaby, although he knew he was a man of no importance, was an amazing juggler.

First he would only balance a tin plate on the tip of his nose. But when the crowd had collected, he would stand on his hands and juggle six copper balls in the air at the same time, catching them with his feet. And sometimes, when he would juggle twelve sharp knives in the air, the villagers would be so delighted that a rain of pennies would fall on his strip of carpet. And when his day's work was over, and he was wearily resting his aching muscles, Barnaby would collect the pennies in his hat, kneel down reverently and thank God for the gift.

Always the people would laugh at his simplicity and every-one would agree that Barnaby would never amount to anything. But all this is about the happy days in Barnaby's life. The springtime days when people were willing to toss a penny to a poor juggler. When winter came, Barnaby had to wrap his juggling equipment in the carpet, and trudge along the roads begging a night's lodging in farmers' barns, or entertaining the servants of some rich nobleman to earn a meal. And Barnaby never thought of complaining – he knew that the winter and the rains were as necessary as the spring sunshine, and he accepted his lot; "for how," Barnaby would say to himself as he trudged along, "could such an ignorant fellow as myself hope for anything better."

And one year in France there was a terrible winter. It began to rain in October and there was hardly a blue sky to be seen by the end of November. And on an evening in early December at the end of a dreary, wet day, as Barnaby trudged along a country road, sad and bent, carrying under his arm the golden balls and knives wrapped up in his old carpet, he met a Monk. Riding a fine white mule, dressed in warm clothes, well-fed and comfortable, the Monk smiled at the sight of Barnaby and called to him: "It's going to be cold before morning .... how would you like to spend the night at the monastery?"

And that night Barnaby found himself seated at the great candle-lit dining hall of the Monastery. Although he sat at the bottom of the long table, together with the servants and beggars, Barnaby thought he had never seen such a wonderful place in his life. The shining faces of fifty Monks relaxing after this day of work and prayer.

Barnaby did not dare to suggest that he should perform his tricks as they would be sacrilege before such men, but as he ate and drank more than he had ever had at a meal for years, a great resolution came over him. Although it made him tremble at his own boldness, as the meal ended, Barnaby suddenly arose, ran around the table down to where the Lordly Abbot sat at the head, and sank to his knees: "Father .... grant my prayer! Let me stay in this wonderful place and work for you! I cannot hope to become one of you, I am too ignorant .... but let me work in the kitchen and the fields, and worship with you in the Chapel!"

The Monk who had met Barnaby on the road turned to the Abbot: "This is a good man, simple and pure of heart." So the Abbot nodded, and Barnaby that night put his juggling equipment under a cot in his own cubicle, and decided that never again would he go back to his old profession.

And in the days that followed, everyone smiled at the eager way he scrubbed the floors and labored throughout the buildings; and everyone smiled at his simplicity. As for Barnaby his face shone with happiness from morning until night.

Until two weeks before Christmas . . . . then Barnaby's joy suddenly turned to misery . For around him he saw every man preparing a wonderful gift to place in the Chapel on Christmas . Brother Maurice , who had the art of illuminating copies of the Bible . And Brother Marbode was completing a marvelous statue of Christ ; Brother Ambrose , who wrote music , and had completed scoring a great hymn to be played on the organ during Christmas services.

All about Barnaby , those educated , trained artists followed their work . . . . each one of them readying a beautiful gift to dedicate to God on Christmas day . And what about Barnaby ? — he could do nothing . "I am but a rough man , unskilled in the arts , and I can write no book , offer no painting or statue or poem . . . . alas . . . . I have no talent , I have no gift worthy of the day ! "

So Barnaby sank deep into sadness and despair . Christmas day came . . . . and the chapel was resplendent with the gifts of the Brothers . . . . the giant organ rang with the new music ; the choir sang the Chorales ; the candles glittered around the great new statue . And Barnaby was not there . . . . he was in his tiny cubicle , praying forgiveness for having no gift to offer .

Then a strange thing happened . On the evening of Christmas day , when the Chapel should have been deserted , one of the Monks came running white-faced and panting with exertion into the private office of the Abbot . He threw open the door without knocking , seized the Abbot by the arms . "Father . . . . a frightful thing is happening . . . . the most terrible sacrilege ever to take place is going on right in our own chapel ! Come ! "

Together the two portly men ran down the corridors , burst through a door , and came out on the balcony at the rear of the chapel . The Monk pointed down toward the altar . The Abbot looked , turned ashen in color . "He is mad ! "

For down below , in front of the altar , was Barnaby . He had spread out his strip of carpet , and kneeling reverently upon it, was actually juggling in the air twelve golden balls! He was giving his old performance.... and giving it beautifully.... his bright knives.... the shining balls, the tin plate balanced on the tip of his nose. And on his face was a look of adoration and joy.

"We must seize him at once," cried the Abbot, and turned for the door. But at that moment a light filled the church.... a brilliant beam of light coming directly from the altar, and.... both the Monks sank to their knees.

For as Barnaby knelt exhausted on his carpet, they saw the Statue of the Virgin Mary move; she came down from her pedestal, and coming to where Barnaby knelt, she took the blue hem of her robe and touched it to his forehead, gently drying the perspiration that glistened there. Then the light dimmed. And up in the choir-balcony the Monk looked at his superior: "God accepted the only gift he had to make."

And the Abbot slowly nodded:

"Blessed are the simple in heart.... for they shall see God."

This old favorite has been universally loved by people of all faiths for its warm portrayal of the spirit that is Christmas. It is presented here with the heartfelt hope that, whatever your belief, you will have found in its message added meaning for your celebration of the birth of the Son of God.

Annie and Willie's Prayer

Sophia P. Snow

'Twas the eve before Christmas;
goodnight had been said,
And Annie and Willie had crept
into bed.
There were tears on their pillows,
and tears in their eyes,
And each little bosom was heaving
with sighs;

*For tonight their stern father's
command had been given
That they should retire precisely
at seven
Instead of at eight; for they
troubled him more
With questions unheard of, than
ever before.*

He told them he thought this
delusion a sin —
No such thing as Santa Claus
ever had been.
And he hoped, after this, he
would never more hear
How he scrambled down chimneys
with presents each year.

*And this was the reason that
two little heads
So restlessly tossed on their
soft downy beds.
Eight, nine, and the clock in the
steeple tolled ton;
Not a word had been spoken by either
till then.*

When Willie's sad face from the
blanket did peep,
And whispered, "Dear Annie, is you
fast asleep?"
"Why, no, brother Willie," a sweet
voice replied,
"I've tried in vain, but I can't
shut my eyes.

*"For somehow, it makes me so sorry
because
Dear Papa said there is no
Santa Claus;
Now we know that there is, and it
can't be denied,
For he came every year before
mamma died;*

"But then I am thinking that she
used to pray,
And God would hear everything
mamma would say.
And perhaps she asked him to send
Santa Claus here,
With the sacks full of presents he
brought every year."

*"Well, why tan't we pray dest as
mamma did then,
And ask Him to send him with
presents aden?"
"I've been thinking so, too," and
without a word more,
Four little bare feet bounded out
on the floor;*

Four little knees the soft carpet
pressed,
And two tiny hands were clasped
close to each breast.
"Now, Willie, you know we must
firmly believe
That the presents we ask for we're
sure to receive;

*"You must wait just as still, till I
say the 'amen'
And by that you will know that your
turn has come then.
Dear Jesus, look down on my brother
and me,
And grant us the favor we are asking
of Thee:*

"I want a wax dolly, a tea set
and ring,
And an ebony work box that shuts
with a spring.
Bless papa, dear Jesus, and cause him
to see
That Santa Claus loves us far
better than he:

*"Don't let him get fretful and
angry again
At dear brother Willie, and Annie.
Amen."
"Pease, Desus, 'et Santa Taus tum
down tonight,
And bring us some presents
before it is light.*

"I want he should div me a
nice 'ittle sed,
With b'ite shiny runners, and all
painted red;
A box full of tandy, a book
and a toy,
Then Desus, I'll be a dood boy.
Amen."

*Their prayers being ended, they raised
up their heads,
And with hearts light and cheerful
again sought their beds.
They were soon lost in slumber,
both peaceful and deep,
And with fairies in dreamland
were roaming in sleep.*

Eight, nine, and the little French
clock had struck ten,
Ere the father had thought of his
children again;
He seems now to hear Annie's
suppressed sighs,
And to see the big tears stand
in Willie's blue eyes.

*"I was harsh with my darlings," he
mentally said,
"And should not have sent them
so early to bed;
But then, I was troubled — my feelings
found vent,
For bank stock today has gone down
ten percent.*

"But of course they've forgotten
their troubles ere this,
And that I denied them the
thrice-asked-for kiss.
But just to make sure I'll steal
up to their door,
For I never spoke harsh to my
darlings before."

*So saying, he softly ascended the
stairs,
And arrived at the door to hear
both of their prayers.
His Annie's "bless papa" draws forth
the big tears,
And Willie's grave promise falls
sweet on his ears.*

"Strange, strange, I'd forgotten,"
said he with a sigh,
"How I longed when a child to have
Christmas draw nigh;
I'll atone for my harshness," he
inwardly said,
"By answering their prayers, ere I
sleep in my bed."

*Then he turned to the stairs, and
softly went down,
Threw off velvet slippers and
silk dressing-gown,
Donned hat, coat and boots, and was
out in the street,
A millionaire facing the cold
driving sleet;*

And as the fond father the picture
surveyed,
He thought for his trouble he had
amply been paid,
And he said to himself, as he brushed
off a tear,
"I'm happier tonight than I've been
for a year.

"I've enjoyed more true pleasure
than ever before,
What care I if bank stock falls
ten percent more;
Hereafter I'll make it a rule,
I believe,
To have Santa Claus visit us each
Christmas Eve."

So thinking, he gently extinguished
the light,
Then tripped down the stairs to
retire for the night.
As soon as the beams of the bright
morning sun
Put the darkness to flight, and the
stars, one by one,

Nor stopped he until he had
bought everything,
From a box full of candy to a
tiny gold ring.
Indeed, he kept adding so much
to his store,
That the various presents
outnumbered a score;

Then homeward he turned with his
holiday load,
And with Aunt Mary's aid in the
nursery 'twas stowed.
Miss dolly was seated beneath
a pine tree,
By the side of a table spread
out for a tea;

A work box well filled in the
center was laid,
And on it the ring for which
Annie had prayed.
A soldier in uniform stood
by a sled,
With bright shining runners, and
all painted red;

There were balls, dogs, and horses,
books pleasing to see,
And birds of all colors were perched
in the tree,
While Santa Claus, laughing, stood
up in the top,
As if getting ready more presents
to drop.

Four little blue eyes out of sleep
open'd wide,
And at the same moment the
presents espied;
Then out of their beds they sprang
with a bound,
And the very gifts prayed for were
all of them found.

They laughed and they cried in their
innocent glee,
And shouted for papa to come
quick and see
What presents old Santa Claus brought
in the night,
(Just the things that they wanted) and
left before light;

"And now," added Annie, in a voice
soft and low,
"You'll believe there's a Santa Claus,
papa, I know."
While dear little Willie climbed up
on his knee,
Determined no secret between them
should be,

And told in soft whispers how Annie
had said,
That their dear blessed mamma so long
ago dead,
Used to kneel down and pray by the
side of her chair,
And that God up in heaven had answered
her prayer!

"Then we dot up and prayed dust as
well as we tould,
And Dod answered our prayers; now
wasn't He dood?"
"I should say that He was if He sent you
all these,
And knew just what presents my children
would please.

("Well, well, let him think so, the dear
little elf;
'Twould be cruel to tell him I did
it myself.")
Blind father! who caused your proud
heart to relent;
And the hasty word spoken so soon
to repent?

'Twas Lord Jesus who bade you
steal softly upstairs,
And made you His agent to answer
their prayers.

A December Night... Long Long Ago.

Mary M. Crawford

The little burro hurried his tired steps, sensing the nearness of the town.

It had been a long two days' journey, although the lovely lady he carried was light as could be, and her voice was music when she spoke to him. (She had even asked his name and called him by it — Jaska.)

Soon now, he thought, comfortingly, they would be warmly housed and ready for the evening meal. *He* could sleep in any shelter, but the lovely lady *must* have a good bed. And the kind man who had walked at Jaska's side all those many miles needed rest, also.

But, on the furthest outskirts of the city, Jaska realized that they were joining many other groups of people. Suddenly the narrow streets seemed to overflow, and Jaska wondered where all the travelers came from.

He stepped even more carefully than he had on the highway, not wanting his lovely lady to be jostled, nor her blue gown to be torn and soiled.

The little burro hesitated at the most crowded point and the man took hold of his bridle and led him into a side street.

Jaska could hear the man asking directions to the nearest inn, but he lifted his head indignantly to the rough answer, "You'll find no beds anywhere. The whole town is overrun at tax-paying time."

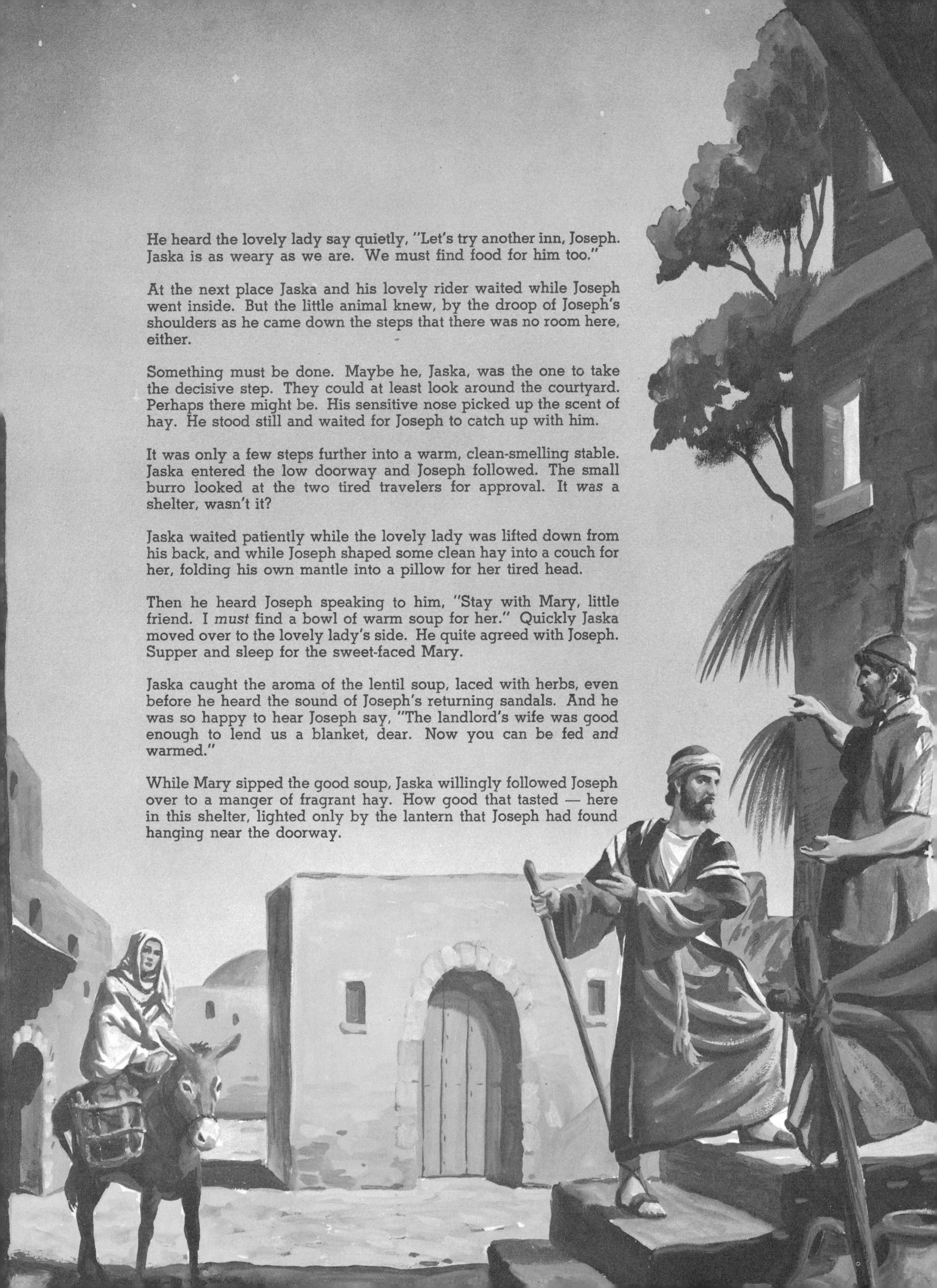

He heard the lovely lady say quietly, "Let's try another inn, Joseph. Jaska is as weary as we are. We must find food for him too."

At the next place Jaska and his lovely rider waited while Joseph went inside. But the little animal knew, by the droop of Joseph's shoulders as he came down the steps that there was no room here, either.

Something must be done. Maybe he, Jaska, was the one to take the decisive step. They could at least look around the courtyard. Perhaps there might be. His sensitive nose picked up the scent of hay. He stood still and waited for Joseph to catch up with him.

It was only a few steps further into a warm, clean-smelling stable. Jaska entered the low doorway and Joseph followed. The small burro looked at the two tired travelers for approval. It *was* a shelter, wasn't it?

Jaska waited patiently while the lovely lady was lifted down from his back, and while Joseph shaped some clean hay into a couch for her, folding his own mantle into a pillow for her tired head.

Then he heard Joseph speaking to him, "Stay with Mary, little friend. I *must* find a bowl of warm soup for her." Quickly Jaska moved over to the lovely lady's side. He quite agreed with Joseph. Supper and sleep for the sweet-faced Mary.

Jaska caught the aroma of the lentil soup, laced with herbs, even before he heard the sound of Joseph's returning sandals. And he was so happy to hear Joseph say, "The landlord's wife was good enough to lend us a blanket, dear. Now you can be fed *and* warmed."

While Mary sipped the good soup, Jaska willingly followed Joseph over to a manger of fragrant hay. How good that tasted — here in this shelter, lighted only by the lantern that Joseph had found hanging near the doorway.

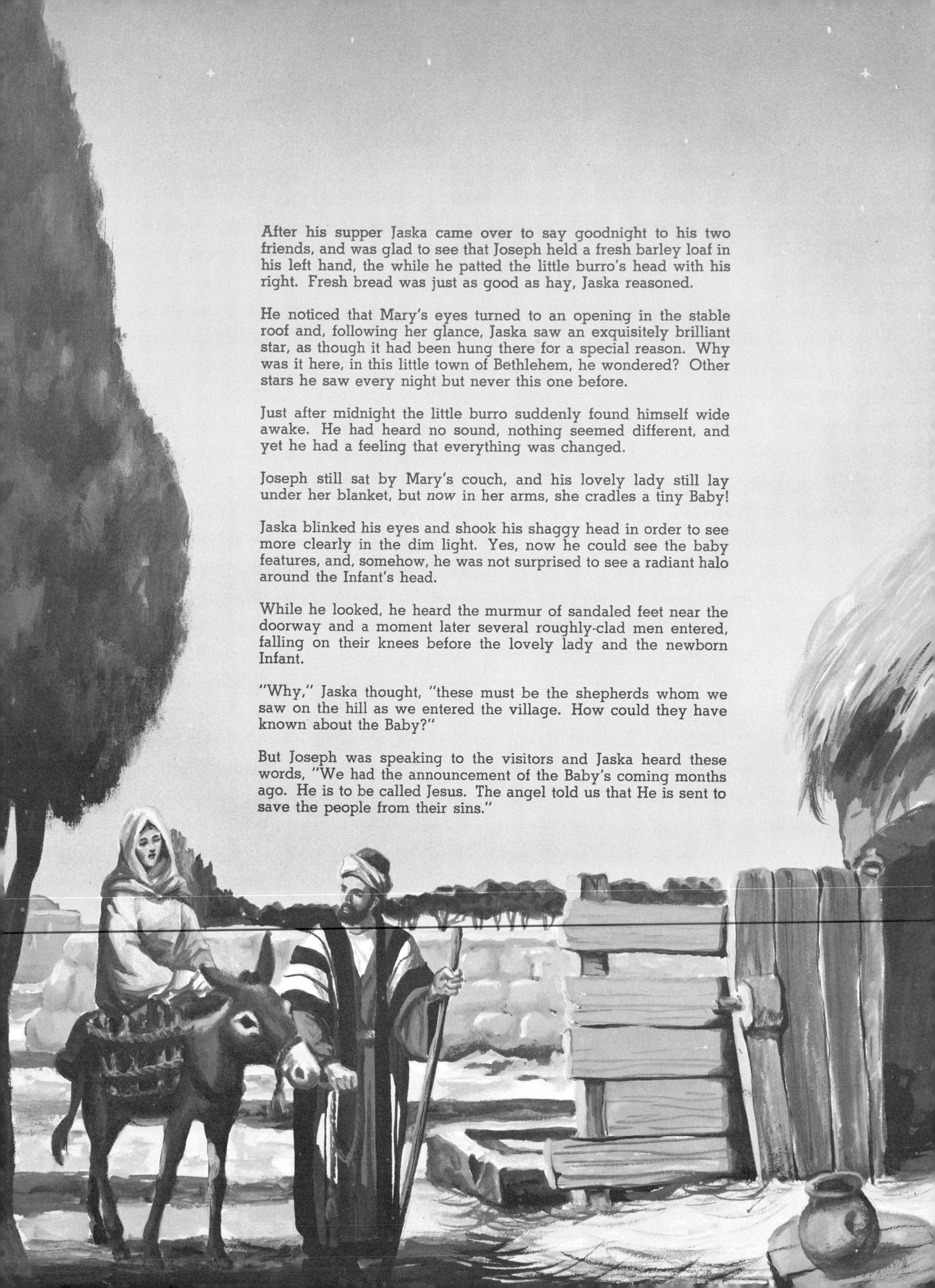

After his supper Jaska came over to say goodnight to his two friends, and was glad to see that Joseph held a fresh barley loaf in his left hand, the while he patted the little burro's head with his right. Fresh bread was just as good as hay, Jaska reasoned.

He noticed that Mary's eyes turned to an opening in the stable roof and, following her glance, Jaska saw an exquisitely brilliant star, as though it had been hung there for a special reason. Why was it here, in this little town of Bethlehem, he wondered? Other stars he saw every night but never this one before.

Just after midnight the little burro suddenly found himself wide awake. He had heard no sound, nothing seemed different, and yet he had a feeling that everything was changed.

Joseph still sat by Mary's couch, and his lovely lady still lay under her blanket, but *now* in her arms, she cradles a tiny Baby!

Jaska blinked his eyes and shook his shaggy head in order to see more clearly in the dim light. Yes, now he could see the baby features, and, somehow, he was not surprised to see a radiant halo around the Infant's head.

While he looked, he heard the murmur of sandaled feet near the doorway and a moment later several roughly-clad men entered, falling on their knees before the lovely lady and the newborn Infant.

"Why," Jaska thought, "these must be the shepherds whom we saw on the hill as we entered the village. How could they have known about the Baby?"

But Joseph was speaking to the visitors and Jaska heard these words, "We had the announcement of the Baby's coming months ago. He is to be called Jesus. The angel told us that He is sent to save the people from their sins."

The shepherds bowed in deepest adoration, and Jaska listened to the last notes of the heavenly chorus as it finished its glorious message.

One of the shepherds explained to Joseph. "We *saw* the angel choir. We could *hear* the beautiful words, 'Glory to God in the Highest, and on earth, Peace, Goodwill toward men.' We had been watching the Star, and then we remembered the Bible prophecy about the birth of a Savior and so we have come to worship Him."

Jaska stood very still, after hearing this, trying to understand what it was all about. He was only a little gray burro, but this much he knew:

Mary and Joseph had been chosen to be a part of a marvelous miracle. The birth of the Baby Jesus in a Bethlehem stable had been foretold many years ago. And, wonder of wonders, he, Jaska, humble Nazareth burro, had been permitted to have a part in this wonderful happening.

He stepped close to Joseph and reveled in the feel of the kind hand on his head.

For the rest of his life he knew he would remember this December night; the stable with the glowing star overhead; the worshiping shepherds; the patient Joseph; the lovely Mary; and above all, the face of the Infant Jesus in the circle of the Heavenly Halo.

The Gifts of the Wise Men

Harvey N. Chinn

Have you ever wondered what Mary and Joseph did with the gold, and frankincense, and myrrh which the wise men brought to them on that Holy Night so many centuries ago? If you'll listen closely, I'll tell you the wonderful story of "what happened to the gifts of the wise men . . ."

The morning after the wise men left, Mary gathered her baby, precious little Jesus, into her arms and went to the entrance of the stable where she gazed out over the quiet little town of Bethlehem. Her eyes felt heavy, for sleep had been impossible with her that night. Before her, the town lay peacefully at rest.

The stars above were like twinkling diamonds on a canopy of velvet. On distant hills, she could easily distinguish the form of sleeping sheep and their shepherds lingering nearby.

For a long time she stood there, seemingly not moving a muscle. But within her heart, thoughts and ideas were racing like a swift stream. Was it a dream? Was it real? Why had the angel come a month ago? Sometimes she thought the angel's visit was only her imagination. Yet what he said had come to pass. And the shepherds! She had been frightened at them, but when Joseph seemed so calm, she welcomed them, too. They had spoken of angels singing "peace on earth." Why couldn't she have peace now?

As her eyes drank in the distant darkness, she could again see those three strange men . . . like kings . . . with long white beards and costly robes. They said they had come from the East to worship a king.

As the dawn broke, Mary could see small puffs of smoke, as the women of Bethlehem were preparing breakfast. How she longed to be back in Nazareth. Behind her, she heard Joseph stirring. But Mary did not move, as one word dominated her mind: Why? Why? Why?

"Don't be afraid, I'll be right back. I must get some food."

"Oh Joseph, what happened? Is it a dream?" Her unsteady voice betrayed her emotions.

"Peace, my child. Go lie down. Try to sleep." The very confidence of his voice soothed her for a moment. Through the portals of the stable, Joseph left for the market place.

Mary returned to the pallet of straw that served as her bed. "Yes, get some sleep." The coarse straw reminded her of her humiliation. Her baby — born in a stable. Aloud she cried, "If this is the Messiah, why was he born here — this stable?" What would she tell her friends when they asked her about his birth? Tears came to her eyes again.

Mary's mind turned to another thought. This was the fourth day now; they only had four more days in which to carry out the age old custom of temple presentation. As she had done many times before, she quoted to herself the scripture:

> *"for a son, or for a daughter, she shall bring a lamb of the first year for a burnt offering, and a young pigeon or a turtledove, for a sin offering, unto the door of the tabernacle of the congregation, unto the priest."*

Where would they find money to make the proper offering for their child? And there would have to be spices to perfume the synagogue, and a payment for the priests. And only four days were left for the Presentation.

Suddenly, Mary half rose to her feet. "The gifts!" Yes, the gifts that the wise men brought. God had provided for His Own. They could take the frankincense and trade part of it for a pair of turtledoves, and use the rest to perfume the temple. For the first time that night, her burden of uncertainty and fear turned into joy.

She could hardly wait for Joseph's return to tell him of her discovery. "Surely God had provided for His Own. Joseph would surely listen." A doubt crossed her mind as she remembered how Joseph had spoken of selling the gifts. She lay back and uttered a prayer.

With that, sleep finally came to Mary.

The smoke from the fire which Joseph had built awakened Mary later in the morning.

"You sleep soundly," was Joseph's only comment, as he stepped outside.

Sleep had refreshed Mary's weakened body. She looked at her sleeping baby, and again breathed the prayer she had prayed a few hours before.

Joseph came back into the stable with a few sticks of firewood, and Mary unfolded her plan for the infant's Presentation.

With his unmovable expression, Joseph drank in each word, not missing a syllable. After she had finished, he continued standing there, staring into the fire. Mary searched his face, hoping for a clue to his answer.

Breaking the silence, he replied in measured syllables. "Mary, the gifts which the strangers brought are valuable. I could sell them, buy my own shop, and be my own master. We could have a better living than before. Those gifts mean the end of poverty. Don't allow sentiment to ruin our future."

"But Joseph, they are not our gifts. They gave them to our baby. You know the law. It will soon be the eighth day. And if he is the Messiah, we should not even think of breaking God's commandments. Oh Joseph, I believe God sent the frankincense to be used at his presentation."

"We have four days to decide." The tone of Joseph's voice left Mary to understand that the subject would be forgotten.

But Mary's persistence triumphed. It was hard for Joseph to give up the idea of a shop of his own, but the weight of Mary's argument, coupled with his own knowledge of the Law, led him on the eighth day to the market place where he traded part of the frankincense for two doves. The rest of the ointment would be used to perfume the temple.

"And when eight days were accomplished . . . they brought him to Jerusalem, to present him to the Lord."

God had provided.

On the night of the presentation, it was Joseph's turn to lay awake, reflecting on the events of the past eight days. He was proud of his son, and he was also proud of himself that he had sacrificed his material wishes in order to keep God's laws. Perhaps he could still buy a shop with the other two gifts.

Suddenly the room was like daylight. Joseph clasped his eyes and called, "Mary."

A Voice said, "Mary can not hear. Fear not, I have come to answer your questions and also to warn you. Your baby Jesus is the Christ Child. His birth is honorable and above that of other men. He was prepared before the ages to save the world from sin. I charge thee to watch over Him, and care for Him, and raise Him as you would your own son. The way will not be easy. I have come to warn you. You must flee this land and go to Egypt. This place is no longer safe for Him. Some day you will return. Do not tarry a single day. God will guide you and provide for you. Peace be unto you. Amen."

The light subsided and the angel was gone.

"Mary!"

"Yes."

"Did you hear what he said?"

"Who?"

"The man . . . the angel. It was an angel. Oh Mary, forgive my doubts. He is the Messiah!"

"You mean the angel spoke to you, too?"

"Yes, he said that we were to watch over Him, and care for Him. He also charged us to flee to Egypt . . ."

"To where?"

"To Egypt!"

"When?"

"He said not to tarry a single day."

This time it was Mary who objected. "But my mother will worry. And our clothes. We must buy another donkey, and food! Joseph, we can't make a trip. A trip takes money, and you said yesterday that you only had seventeen shekels. That won't buy a donkey. Oh Joseph, it was only a dream."

"No. An angel told me to take care of Him as I would my own son. I dare not disobey."

"But the money?"

"He said that God will provide."

"But Joseph, I am so weak. The babe is so small. Surely you are mistaken. And the money, where . . . ?"

"Mary! You are right. Those gifts are from God." A great light broke across Joseph's face, as the words gushed from his mouth.

"Jehovah sent those wise men. That chest of gold nuggets was meant for this trip. They will take care of us for two years, maybe even three or four. I will go as soon as day breaks and buy a donkey, and clothes, and food. And to think, we were chosen by God to. . . ." Joseph's voice trailed off in wonderment and amazement.

Neither Mary nor Joseph slept the rest of that night. Long before daybreak, both were up, Mary packing their meager belongings, and Joseph eager to be off to the market place to get first choice on the donkeys which would be offered for sale that day.

By noon, more than a dozen miles lay between the Holy Family and Bethlehem, and they "departed into Egypt."

God had provided.

* * *

Mary and Joseph spent over two years in Egypt. They used the gold sparingly and wisely in buying the necessities of life. It lasted three years. When only two nuggets were left in the chest, Joseph felt that the very fact that the gold was running low was God's sign that they were to return.

The journey back to Palestine was a pleasant one for the family. The scenery was enchanting and the weather ideal. Jesus would run along beside the donkeys and play, and ask many questions about the countryside. He repeatedly asked why they had to leave "home," as he knew Egypt.

At last they came to Nazareth, found a home, and fell into the routine of village life. Joseph found employment in the nearby village of Sephoris, which was being rebuilt after a terrible destruction by Roman soldiers.

The years came and went for Jesus as they do for anyone. As a boy, he went to the synagogue with the rest of the village youth. He helped his father, played with the other boys and girls, and enjoyed life.

All Nazareth knew that there was something different about Mary's son, but Mary alone knew the secret. When Joseph died, the town wags remembered Jesus' words about doing his father's business. Even Mary finally convinced herself that Jesus had been talking about assuming the business of Joseph.

Then had come the inevitable day, when Jesus laid down his carpenter's tools, turned the shop over to James, bid farewell to Mary, and left home. He traveled southward to Jerusalem, then crossed over to the Jordan, where he was baptized by his cousin, John.

Jesus' departure made a big change in Mary's life. When the news came that Jesus was surpassing even John in popularity, Mary withdrew more and more unto herself and her memories.

Mary often reflected about the early years of Jesus' life. Although she had never told him about the visits of the angel, or why they had lived in Egypt, she realized that he knew. She was proud of his achievements.

Yet, Mary was still troubled. Not a week passed, but that she went to her closet and there took out the chest that had once housed the gold. Now it contained a sealed flask, wrapped in heavy towelling. The flask contained the myrrh, the last of the three gifts that the three strange men had given to her. The chest had become to her a shrine, to which she went when her thoughts turned toward her son. It was the only visible token of his childhood.

* * *

It was the evening before the celebration of the Passover. Tomorrow she was going to Jerusalem to see her son. As she thought of Jesus, she again went to the closet, took out the chest, and unwrapped the flask. It contained the myrrh — the ointment for the dead! She clutched it in her hands and shuddered as portions of Scripture came to her mind. "He was cut off from the land of the living." "He is brought as a lamb to the slaughter."

She recalled vividly how these words had struck her when she had taught them to Jesus as a boy. For years, she had tried to tell herself that they were not

a prophecy about her son. She had tried to put the thought out of her mind, but to no avail. Tonight, as she touched the myrrh, all of these thoughts of death came back to her. Somehow she knew that Death was at hand.

The next few days were as a blur in the mind of Mary. The trip to Jerusalem had upset her. Her friends had tried to shield her from the events of the day. But Mary knew — she knew that they were killing her son. All the events — the excitement of the town, the talk of betrayals, and trials — all told her that they were taking her son away from her. But through it all, only one thing gave Mary consolation — the flask of myrrh. Somehow that vessel told Mary that it was in the will of God that Jesus must die. She realized that within a few hours, that myrrh would anoint the broken body of her son. In a sense, the myrrh was now anointing Mary's heart, for it told her that God had also provided for his death.

Despite her friends' protests, Mary attended the execution. She saw the frenzied crowd as they yelled at the sight of Jesus' blood. She witnessed with her own eyes the agony, the suffering, and the pain of Jesus, as he hung upon the cross. She shuddered as the spear tore into his flesh. With her own ears, she heard Him say, "It is finished," and she saw his head drop to his chest.

And all the while, Mary clasped the flask to herself and repeated, "God has provided. God will provide."

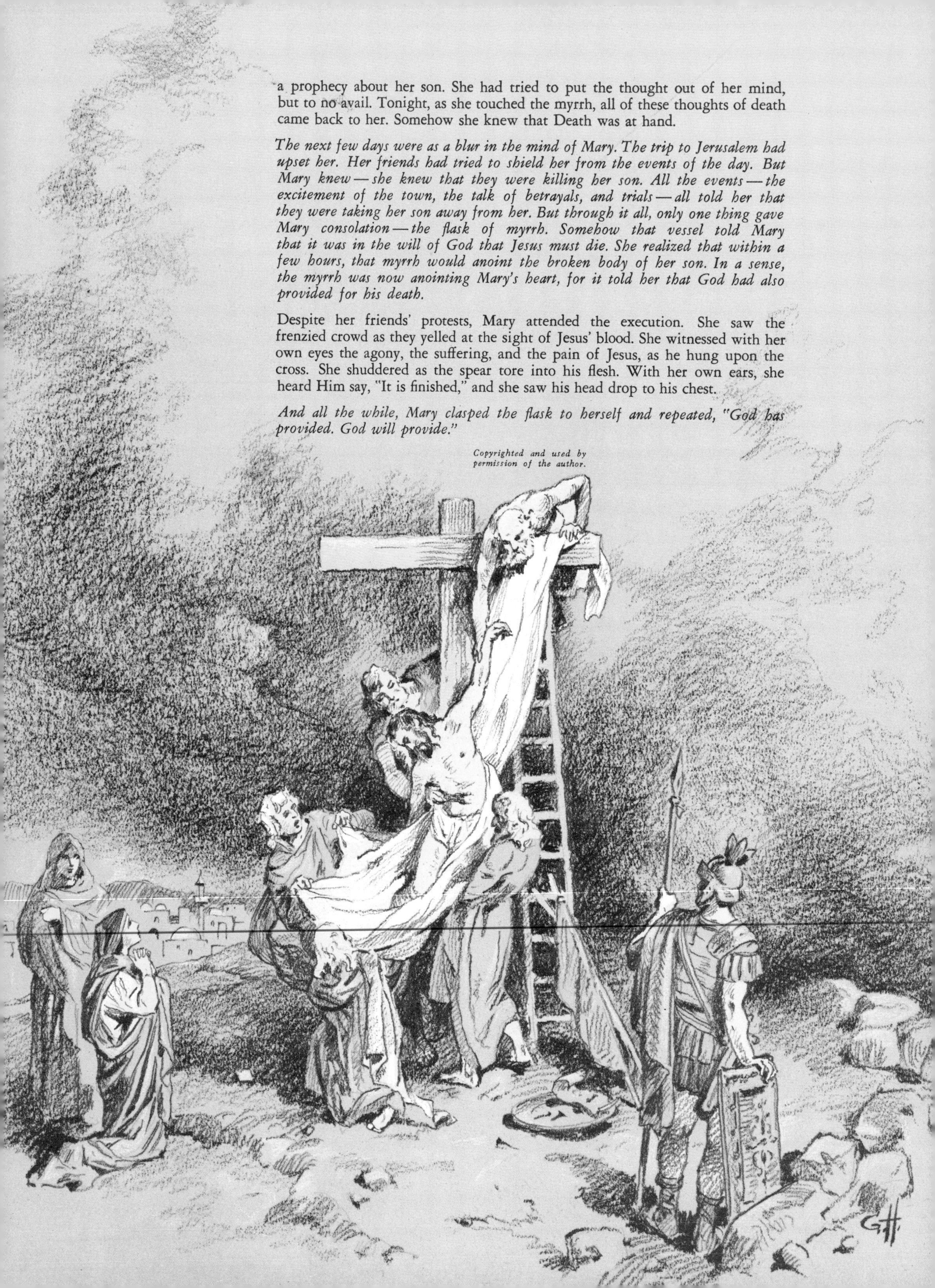

One Solitary Life

Here is a man who was born in an obscure village, the child of a peasant woman. He grew up in another obscure village. He worked in a carpenter shop until He was thirty, and then for three years He was an itinerant preacher. He never wrote a book. He never held an office.

He never owned a home. He never set foot inside a big city. He never travelled two hundred miles from the place where He was born. He had no credentials but Himself.

He had nothing to do with this world except the naked power of His divine manhood. While still a young man, the tide of popular opinion turned against Him. His friends ran away. One of them denied Him. He was turned over to His enemies. He went through the mockery of a trial. He was nailed upon a cross between two thieves.

His executioners gambled for the only piece of property He had on earth while He was dying — and that was His coat. When He was dead He was taken down and laid in a borrowed grave through the pity of a friend.

Nineteen wide centuries have come and gone and today He is the centerpiece of the human race and the leader of progress. I am far within the mark when I say that all the armies that ever marched, and all the navies that ever were built, and all the parliaments that ever sat, and all the kings that ever reigned, put together have not affected the life of man upon this earth as powerfully as that One Solitary Life.

Our sincere appreciation to the unknown author.

The First Christmas Tree

● *Rose Fyleman*

This story of the First Christmas Tree was told me by the Fairy Queen herself, so you may be quite sure it is a true one. Here it is.

Once upon a time there lived in the middle of a forest a poor woodcutter.

He had one little daughter called Annis, whom he loved dearly. Annis was a dear little girl, kind and gentle.

She was very fond of all the woodland creatures, and they in turn knew and loved her well. The fairies loved her also. They used to dance on the top of the low stone wall that went round the little garden in front of the cottage.

"Annis! Annis!" they would call to her while she was busy helping her mother in the kitchen. But she would shake her head.

"I can't come. I'm busy," she would answer.

But at night-time, when she was fast asleep under her red quilt, they would come tapping at the little window.

"Annis! Annis!"

Then she would slip out of bed and run quickly downstairs with her bare feet, and off with the fairies into the moon-shining woods.

But the next day she was never sure whether it had been a dream or reality.

That was in the summer.

It was winter now, and very cold. The sky was dark and heavy with coming snow.

Every evening, all through the winter, Annis would hang a little lantern with a candle in it on the small fir-tree that grew just inside the garden-gate. Her father could see it as he came home through the trees. It was a little bright welcome for him even before he reached home.

On Christmas Eve he went to work as usual. He came home for his dinner at midday and started back early. He was at work quite a long way off.

"I shall finish there to-day," he said to his wife as he left the house. "Then I shall come nearer home. If the snow comes it will be difficult to find the way in the dark evenings."

And that very day the snow began. All the afternoon it fell in great, soft flakes.

Down, down, down . . . It seemed as if the whole sky were falling in little bits.

The woodcutter worked hard in the fading light.

It was quite dark by the time he had finished, and he had to keep shaking the snow from his shoulders and from his old hat.

The wood was all neatly stacked in the little shed which had been built up there to house it.

He started off home with a sigh of relief, smiling to himself as he thought of his warm hearth and the bowl of hot porridge waiting for him on the hob, and of little Annis knitting in the chimney-corner.

But presently — how it happened I know not, for he knew the forest well, and the snow had almost stopped falling, and the moon was shining — he found that he had lost his way.

He was quite cheerful at first. "In a minute I shall find the path again," he said. But many minutes passed and he did not find it. A cloud came over the moon; the snow began to fall again more thickly. It was like a moving, whirling mist where the trees stood less close together.

The woodcutter began to lose heart.

Then suddenly, he saw a light ahead of him on one of the fir-trees.

"Can I be so near home?" he said, half-bewildered. But when he came near he found that it was not a fir-tree in his own garden that was lit up, but an ordinary forest-tree. Little lights twinkled and glittered on its branches, burning brightly and steadily in spite of the falling snow. The woodcutter rubbed his eyes. "If this be wicked magic," he thought, "it will now disappear." But the lights burned more brightly than ever, and as he looked about he saw in the distance another tree lit up in the same way. Then he understood.

"It is the good fairies helping me," he said, and trudged off cheerily in the direction of the second tree.

And when he looked back, the first one had already grown dark again. But when he reached the second tree, another was shining ahead to show him the way.

And so he went on from tree to tree until at last he was guided safely home to Annis' little lantern in his own garden.

And always after that he used to put lights on a little fir-tree on Christmas Eve in memory of the time when the fairies saved him from being lost in the forest. And so the custom began, and because it was such a pretty one, and because the fairies so willed it, it spread, and to-day the fairy Christmas tree is to be found all over the world in houses where there are children and where the fairies come. . . .

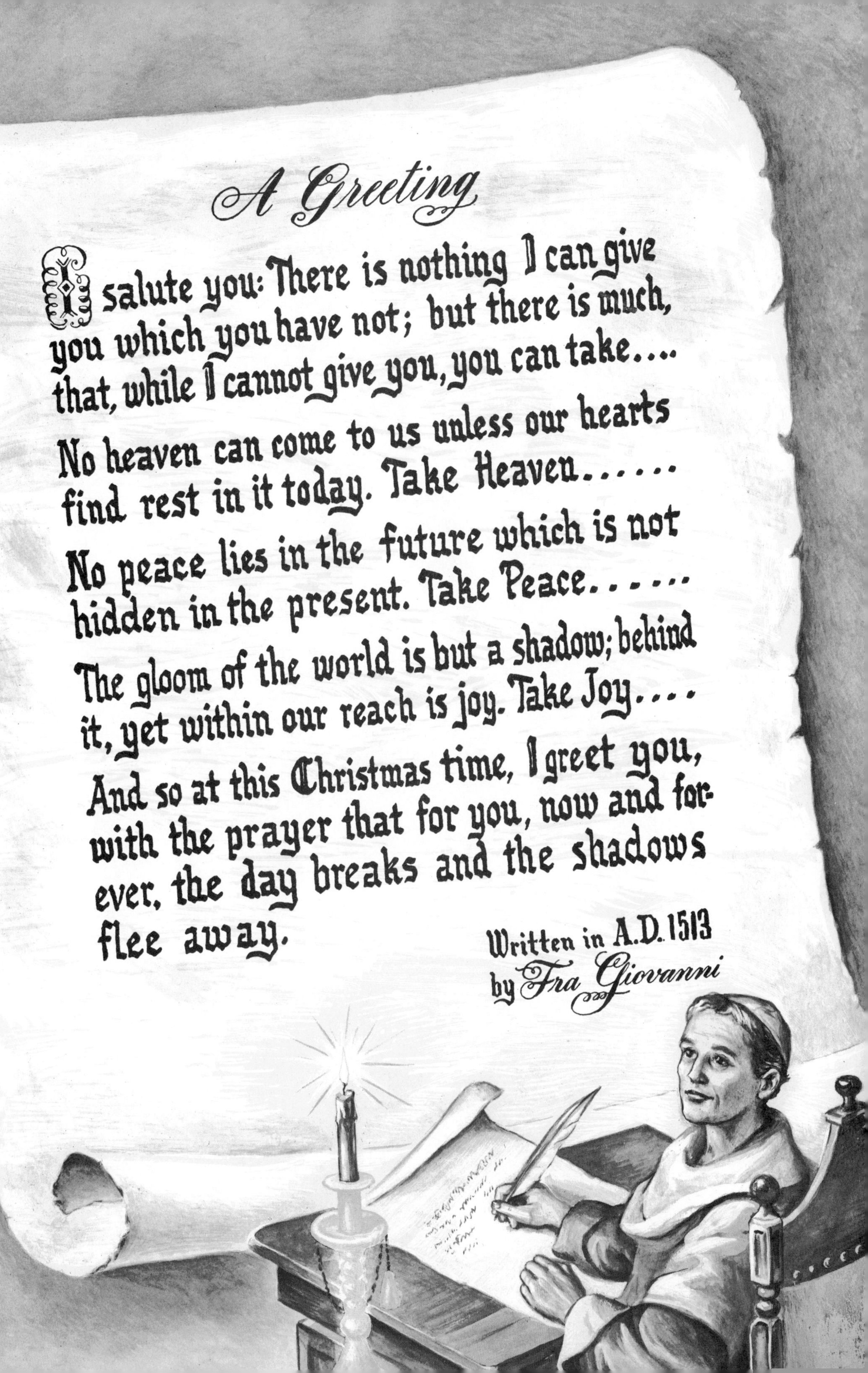
A Greeting
I salute you: There is nothing I can give
you which you have not; but there is much,
that, while I cannot give you, you can take....
No heaven can come to us unless our hearts
find rest in it today. Take Heaven......
No peace lies in the future which is not
hidden in the present. Take Peace......
The gloom of the world is but a shadow; behind
it, yet within our reach is joy. Take Joy....
And so at this Christmas time, I greet you,
with the prayer that for you, now and forever, the day breaks and the shadows
flee away.
Written in A.D. 1513
by Fra Giovanni

May we tell you about more Ideals publications?

64 nostalgic pages
size 8 1/2 by 11 inches

$1.50
per copy

cellophaned
HARD BOUND cover

CHRISTMAS MEMORY LANE

Walk along the lane to Christmas of yesteryear. Happy days of the long ago recall the memory-laden Christmases of days gone by. The excitement, the anticipation, the thrill of "Christmas in the air", that you experienced are portrayed in poetry, prose and colorful art reproductions. A joy to read, a book to treasure.

80 inspiring pages
size 8 1/2 by 11 inches

$1.50
per copy

cellophaned
HARD BOUND cover

RELIGIOUS CHRISTMAS STORIES FOR CHILDREN

A most interesting book that will bring happiness to all young children during the Christmas season. A lovely collection of Christmas stories — some new, some your very own long-time favorites. A cherished book for children of all ages — with stories that will be remembered all of their lives.

24 colorful pages
size 8 1/2 by
11 inches

$1.50
per copy

cellophaned
HARD BOUND cover

THE NIGHT BEFORE CHRISTMAS

The wonderful old, old story by Clement C. Moore — that has fascinated and thrilled and sparked the dreams of children for generations. Brand new — from cover to cover — with twenty-four full page color paintings made especially for this issue by Donald Mills. A book that will bring exciting happiness to every child.

48 magnificent
pages
size 8 1/2 by
11 inches

$1.50
per copy

cellophaned
HARD BOUND cover

THUS IT IS WRITTEN

Embellished and inscribed on parchment, like ancient manuscripts, these exquisitely beautiful engrossments have thrilled many thousands as they have been exhibited throughout the entire country. Each scroll, its designs, symbols, colors and forms and meanings are described to you. We are proud to present them in book form for your inspiration.

Your Book Dealer or Book Department can supply – or obtain these books for you!

This information section may be removed without damage to the rest of your book

This Christmas — give a distinctive gift — — —

72 exquisite pages
size 8 1/2 by 11 inches
$1.50 per copy
cellophaned HARD BOUND cover

THE TRUE RELIGIOUS CHRISTMAS
A colorful book dedicated to the true reverent spirit of the Christmas season. Poems and prose, beautiful full color art reproductions, lend themselves to a thoughtful presentation of inspiration and devotion. The happy hours of pleasure make this book a delightful reading experience as each page tells of the religious significance of this Holy Season.

96 interesting pages
size 8 1/2 by 11 inches
$1.50 per copy
cellophaned HARD BOUND cover

THE HAPPY CHRISTMAS STORY BOOK
Many, many hours of childhood happiness are packed into this new BIG book of Christmas stories — filled with the old, old favorites — and new ones, too. These are stories to be read aloud. Each story is beautifully and artistically illustrated with specially prepared art. A children's gift that will be read, enjoyed and cherished for years to come.

48 melodious pages
size 8 1/2 by 11 inches
$1.50 per copy
cellophaned HARD BOUND cover

CHRISTMAS CAROLS THAT NEVER GROW OLD
Favorite Christmas hymns and carols are reproduced in an artistic and colorful way to bring a tradition of song to your home this year. The melodious carols will add to the joy of Christmas and will bring back glowing memories in song of Christmases past. Make Christmas a season of song.

48 colorful pages
size 8 1/2 by 11 inches
$1.50 per copy
cellophaned HARD BOUND cover

A TREASURE OF CHRISTMAS RELIGIOUS ART
A revised and enlarged book — more beautiful than ever — each colorful art masterpiece brings to you the famous-well-loved-Christmas religious art — by the Old Masters, as well as by the talented contemporary artists. You will acclaim each exquisite page "*Beautiful Enough to Frame*".

IDEALS PUBLISHING CO.
Milwaukee, Wis.

America's most beautiful and wholesome publications

Your Personal Order

Important — Items checked here will be sent directly to you at the address below. Your ZIP code is an important part of your address — it insures rapid accurate handling of your mail

YOUR NAME ______

ADDRESS ______

CITY ______

STATE ______ ZIP CODE ( )

ITEM		QUANTITY	AMOUNT
CHRISTMAS MEMORY LANE	@$1.50		
RELIGIOUS CHRISTMAS STORIES FOR CHILDREN	@$1.50		
THE NIGHT BEFORE CHRISTMAS	@$1.50		
THUS IT IS WRITTEN	@$1.50		
THE TRUE RELIGIOUS CHRISTMAS	@$1.50		
THE HAPPY CHRISTMAS STORY BOOK	@$1.50		
CHRISTMAS CAROLS THAT NEVER GROW OLD	@$1.50		
A TREASURE OF CHRISTMAS RELIGIOUS ART	@$1.50		
DICKENS' CHRISTMAS CAROL	@$1.50		
CHRISTMAS STORIES THAT NEVER GROW OLD	@$1.50		
CHRISTMAS AROUND THE WORLD	@$1.50		
JOLLY OLD SANTA CLAUS	@$1.50		
WE SAY OUR PRAYERS	@$1.50		
WORDS ETERNAL	@$1.50		
FRIENDSHIP	@$1.50		
IDEALS SCRAP BOOK	@$1.50		
THE CIRCUS	@$1.50		
FLAGS OF AMERICA	@$1.50		
	TOTAL		

Your Gift Order

To: ______

ADDRESS ______

CITY ______

STATE ______ ZIP CODE ( )

from ______

ITEM		QUANTITY	AMOUNT
CHRISTMAS MEMORY LANE	@$1.50		
RELIGIOUS CHRISTMAS STORIES FOR CHILDREN	@$1.50		
THE NIGHT BEFORE CHRISTMAS	@$1.50		
THUS IT IS WRITTEN	@$1.50		
THE TRUE RELIGIOUS CHRISTMAS	@$1.50		
THE HAPPY CHRISTMAS STORY BOOK	@$1.50		
CHRISTMAS CAROLS THAT NEVER GROW OLD	@$1.50		
A TREASURE OF CHRISTMAS RELIGIOUS ART	@$1.50		
DICKENS' CHRISTMAS CAROL	@$1.50		
CHRISTMAS STORIES THAT NEVER GROW OLD	@$1.50		
CHRISTMAS AROUND THE WORLD	@$1.50		
JOLLY OLD SANTA CLAUS	@$1.50		
WE SAY OUR PRAYERS	@$1.50		
WORDS ETERNAL	@$1.50		
FRIENDSHIP	@$1.50		
IDEALS SCRAP BOOK	@$1.50		
THE CIRCUS	@$1.50		
FLAGS OF AMERICA	@$1.50		
	TOTAL		

Your Book Dealer or Book Department can supply — or obtain these books for you!

Words Eternal

We are proud and honored to reproduce in book form for your pleasure and inspiration this collection of engrossments by the artist Kate K. Ball.

Embellished and inscribed on parchment, like ancient manuscripts, using techniques that are reminiscent of the 16th century calligraphers, these scrolls are a stimulating experience in Biblical presentations.

Each decorative scroll is described relating to the meaningful colors, designs, symbols and forms.

A unique and exquisitely beautiful book — each page beautiful enough to frame.

52 magnificent pages

$1.50 per copy

cellophaned HARD BOUND cover

We Say Our Prayers

Every parent will want to teach these simple and very beautiful prayers that are colorfully illustrated in this lovely book.

Prayers at bedtime, grace before meals, prayers for the day — and prayers for the night. Truly a rich heritage of the well-known and well-loved prayers from generation to generation.

An interesting way for children — of all ages — to learn meaningful expressions of faith and trust that will live with them all of their lives.

An ideal gift book for all occasions.

56 exquisite pages

$1.50 per copy

cellophaned HARD BOUND cover

Friendship

To capture the warm spirit and true meaning of this theme, a special book—"FRIENDSHIP"—has been prepared. Selections of the best poetry and prose, together with the finest full color reproductions of fine paintings and the best of the photographers' skill, create a feeling of honest, sincere friendliness in this book.

Each artistic page expresses the feeling of FRIENDSHIP that so often is hard to put into words.

"FRIENDSHIP" will be one of your most treasured books — you and your friends will be thoroughly pleased with this quality publication.

You will want a copy for yourself and additional ones as gifts for those who hold a favored spot in your heart. Keep "FRIENDSHIP" books on hand for those occasions when you wish to present "just the right" gift.

52 lovely pages

$1.50 per copy

cellophaned HARD BOUND cover

IDEALS PUBLISHING CO.
Milwaukee, Wis.

— — — instead of an expensive one!

48 lovely pages size 8 1/2 by 11 inches
$1.50 per copy
cellophaned HARD BOUND cover

DICKENS' CHRISTMAS CAROL
The dramatic spine-tingling story of Scrooge, Bob Cratchit, and lovable Tiny Tim is retold by Charles Dickens in this special artistic edition. You will savor the "plum pudding" atmosphere, the true Dickens flavor of this enchanting story that ends happily with Tiny Tim's "God bless us everyone".

44 delightful pages size 8 1/2 by 11 inches
$1.50 per copy
cellophaned HARD BOUND cover

CHRISTMAS STORIES THAT NEVER GROW OLD
A delightful collection of the favorite Christmas stories that have enraptured readers for generations. Colorful pages depict scenes from legends and tales that we associate so dearly with the exciting and inspiring season of Christmas — a joy to read aloud and a book that will add to your Christmas tradition.

36 fascinating pages size 8 1/2 by 11 inches
$1.50 per copy
cellophaned HARD BOUND cover

CHRISTMAS AROUND THE WORLD
The festivities — the traditions — the pageantries — the inspiring Christmas observances by the peoples of SPAIN — FINLAND — GERMANY — SWEDEN — SERBIA — IRELAND — BELGIUM — and many others — a total of *32* different countries are presented in this interesting book.

44 exciting pages size 8 1/2 by 11 inches
$1.50 per copy
cellophaned HARD BOUND cover

JOLLY OLD SANTA CLAUS
An exciting adventure for children of all ages — awakening the vivid happy dreams of childhood, Santa and Toyland. Santa and his mischievous elves prepare for the long exciting journey to the hearts of young ones — and the rest of the joyous trip that Santa loves each year.

Your Book Dealer or Book Department can supply — or obtain these books for you!

America's most beautiful and wholesome publications

THE CIRCUS

Clowns, trapeze artists, animal trainers, elephants and all the other thrilling acts — they're all here in one enchanting book.

Imagine yourself in the best seat under the big top with the show about to begin — the ringmaster is introducing the first stupendous, super-colossal attraction . . .

Relive this enjoyable moment and all the wonderful events that make up a "day at the circus". These cherished memories will come to life again with your first glimpse of "THE CIRCUS".

68 colorful pages

Colorful pages throughout — reproductions of the finest in circus art — pictures and paintings of most of your favorites — poems and articles that will please the "young in heart" — this is "THE CIRCUS".

Unique in its presentation — "THE CIRCUS" is a truly authentic look at the tradition-steeped world that we all at one time wished to adopt for our career. Order your copy today and . . .

Send additional copies to your friends, relatives and that "little someone special" whose eyes you know will light up with wonder and delight at these beautiful pages.

$1.50 per copy

cellophaned HARD BOUND cover

96 interesting pages

Scrap Book

The new "IDEALS SCRAP BOOK" has been specially prepared to acquaint our new readers with the type and quality of inspiring poetry, prose, photographs, art that are featured in EVERY issue of IDEALS.

Each issue of IDEALS features one principal theme — some of the subjects have included CHRISTMAS — EASTER — FAMILY — THANKSGIVING — VACATION — INSPIRATION.

IDEALS SCRAP BOOKS contain pages of colorful beauty-poetry and prose depicting the glorious seasons of the year — Spring and Easter — Summer and Vacation — Autumn and Harvest — Winter and Christmas — true wholesome, old-fashioned nostalgic remembrances of the happy days of long ago.

Order your IDEALS SCRAP BOOKS TODAY — and keep a supply on hand of these lovely gift books.

These issues will meet your exacting demands for a quality gift to present for special HOLIDAYS — BIRTHDAYS — GRADUATIONS — ANNIVERSARIES and other important days.

$1.50 per copy

cellophaned HARD BOUND cover

Flags of America

A series of TWENTY rich oil paintings prepared especially for this book by the famous artist GEORGE HINKE tells dramatically the exciting story that surrounds each of the flags that have flown over America.

These paintings portray dramatically the twenty principal flags that have reflected the growth and development of our great country — from the time of the Norsemen until TODAY.

Walk along the historic paths trod by courageous explorers, determined Pilgrims, fearless pioneers, inspired statesmen — and the sturdy men and women who built a new country — founded upon the principles of freedom and justice.

FLAGS OF AMERICA will impart to you — and awaken in your children — the basic principles for which America stands — freedom — justice — opportunity — democracy — accomplishments — and dedication.

You must SEE this exquisite book to appreciate its timeliness, its historic beauty and its importance — especially in these moving times.

$1.50 per copy

cellophaned HARD BOUND cover

48 historic pages

IDEALS PUBLISHING CO.
Milwaukee, Wis.

Your Book Dealer or Book Department can supply — or obtain these books for you!